Dear parents,

As a mom and as an educator, I am very excit[...] [b]ook series with all of you. I developed this series for my two kids in elementary school, utilizing all of my knowledge and experience that I have gained while studying and working in the fields of Elementary Education and Gifted Education in South Korea as well as in the United States.

While raising my kids in the U.S., I had great disappointment and dissatisfaction about the math curriculum in the public schools. Based on my analysis, students cannot succeed in math with the current school curriculum because there is no sequential building up of fundamental skills. This is akin to building a castle on sand. So instead, I wanted to find a good workbook, but couldn't. And I also tried to find a tutor, but the price was too expensive for me. These are the reasons why I decided to make the Tiger Math series on my own.

The Tiger Math series was designed based on my three beliefs toward elementary math education.

1. It is extremely important to build foundation of math by acquiring a sense of numbers and mastering the four operation skills in terms of addition, subtraction, multiplication, and division.
2. In math, one should go through all steps in order, step by step, and cannot jump from level 1 to 3.
3. Practice math every day, even if only for 10 minutes.

If you feel that you don't know where your child should start, just choose a book in the Tiger Math series where your child thinks he/she can complete most of the material. And encourage your child to do only 2 sheets every day. When your child finishes the 2 sheets, review them together and encourage your child about his/her daily accomplishment.

I hope that the Tiger Math series can become a stepping stone for your child in gaining confidence and for making them interested in math as it has for my kids. Good luck!

Michelle Y. You, Ph.D.
Founder and CEO of Tiger Math

ACT scores show that only one out of four high school graduates are prepared to learn in college. This preparation needs to start early. In terms of basic math skills, being proficient in basic calculation means a lot. Help your child succeed by imparting basic math skills through hard work.

Sungwon S. Kim, Ph.D.
Engineering Professor

Level A – 3: Plan of Study

| Goal A | Practice counting, writing, reading, and ordering numbers up to 110. (Week 1 ~ 2) |

| Goal B | Practice adding the numbers of 1 and 2 to the numbers in between 1 and 15. (Week 3 ~ 4) |

Week 1

Day	Tiger Session		Topic	Goal
Mon	81	82	Numbers up to 90	Counting, reading, writing, ordering numbers
Tue	83	84		
Wed	85	86		
Thu	87	88		
Fri	89	90		

Week 2

Day	Tiger Session		Topic	Goal
Mon	91	92	Numbers up to 110	Counting, reading, writing, ordering numbers
Tue	93	94		
Wed	95	96		
Thu	97	98		
Fri	99	100		

Week 3

Day	Tiger Session		Topic	Goal
Mon	101	102	Adding 1	Pre-activity
Tue	103	104	Adding 1	Pre-activity
Wed	105	106	Adding 1	$(1 \sim 7) + 1$
Thu	107	108	Adding 1	$(1 \sim 10) + 1$
Fri	109	110	Adding 1	$(1 \sim 15) + 1$

Week 4

Day	Tiger Session		Topic	Goal
Mon	111	112	Adding 2	Pre-activity
Tue	113	114	Adding 2	$(1 \sim 7) + 1$
Wed	115	116	Adding 2	$(1 \sim 15) + 2$
Thu	117	118	Adding 2	$(1 \sim 15) + 2$
Fri	119	120	Adding 2	$(1 \sim 15) + 2$

Week 1

This week's goal is to practice counting, writing, reading, and ordering numbers up to 90.

Tiger Session

Monday	81	82
Tuesday	83	84
Wednesday	85	86
Thursday	87	88
Friday	89	90

81 Numbers up to 90 ①

15
17 seventeen

♠ **Count and write the number of objects.**

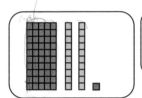
Seventy one

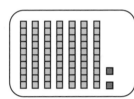
Seventy two

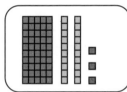
Seventy three

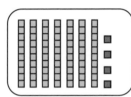
Seventy four

$10×5=50$
$10+10+$
$+10+10+$
$+10=50$

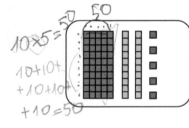
Seventy five

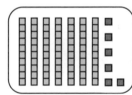
Seventy six

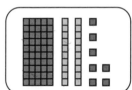
Seventy seven

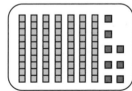
Seventy eight

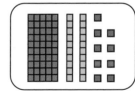
Seventy nine

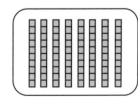
Eighty

78 seventy-eight

♠ **Count and write the number of objects.**

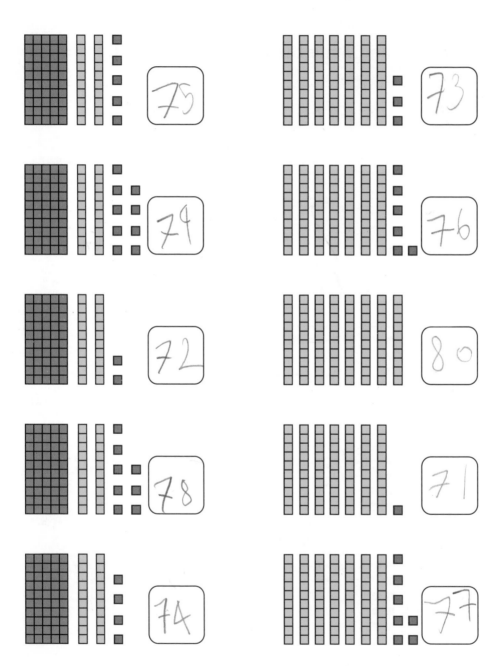

75

73

79

76

72

80

78

71

74

77

82 Numbers up to 90 ②

♠ Write the number which comes right <u>after</u> the given number.

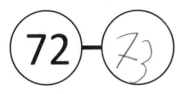

Read

♠ Write the number which comes right <u>before</u> the given number.

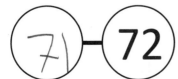

♠ Write the missing numbers.

67 – 68 – 69 – 70 – 71

70 – 71 – 72 – 73 – 74

73 74 75 76 77

76 – 77 – 78 – 79 – 80

78 79 80 81 82

83 Numbers up to 90 ③

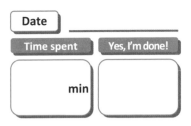

♠ **Count and write the number of objects.**

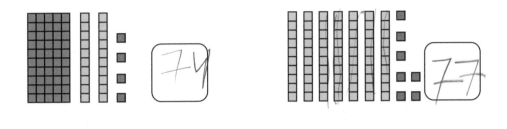

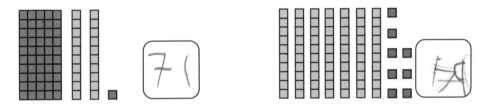

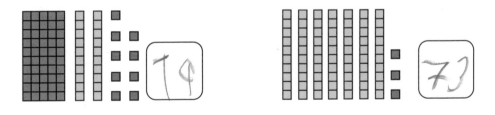

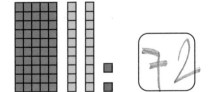

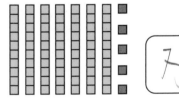

♠ Count and write the numbers of objects.

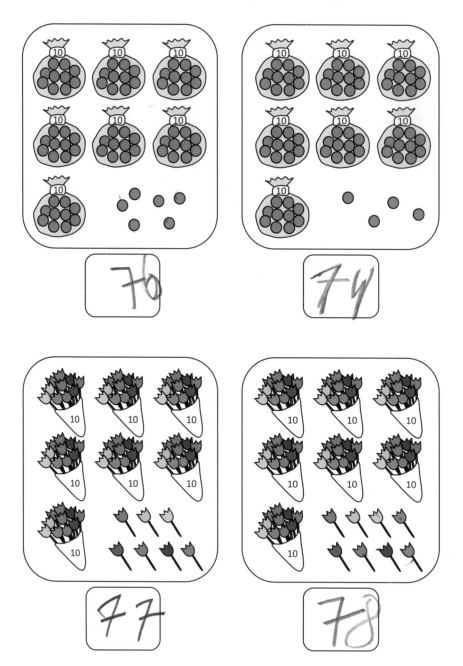

76

74

77

78

Date _____

Time spent _____ min

Yes, I'm done!

♠ **Write the missing numbers.**

71	72	73	74	75
76	77	78	79	80

71	72	73	74	75
76	77	78	79	80

71	72	73	74	75
76	77	78	79	80

♠ Write the missing numbers.

61	62	63	64	65
66	67	68	69	70
71	72	73	74	75
76	77	78	79	80
81	82	83	84	85
86	87	88	89	90

♠ Rewrite the given numbers from the smallest to the largest.

73   72   75   74

72 — 73 — 74 — 75

85 **Numbers up to 90 ⑤**

♠ Count and write the number of objects.

 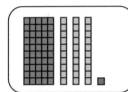
Eighty one

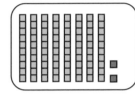
Eighty two

 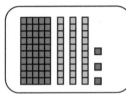
Eighty three

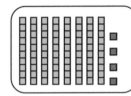
Eighty four

 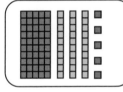
Eighty five

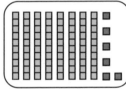
Eighty six

 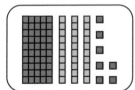
Eighty seven

Eighty eight

 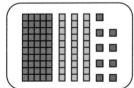
Eighty nine

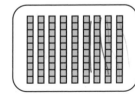
Ninety

♠ **Count and write the number of objects.** $8 \times 10 = 80$

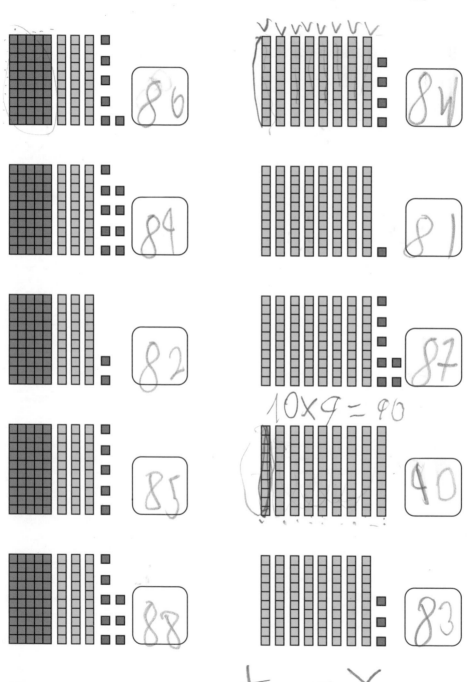

$10 \times 9 = 90$

$+ - \times$

86 **Numbers up to 90** ⑥

♠ Write the number which comes right <u>after</u> the given number.

81 – 82 87 – 88

89 – 90 84 – 85

♠ Write the number which comes right <u>before</u> the given number.

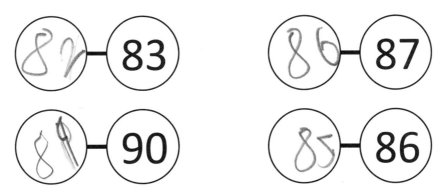

82 – 83 86 – 87

89 – 90 85 – 86

♠ Write the missing numbers.

75 – 76 – 77 – 78 – 79

77 – 78 – 79 – 80 – 81

80 – 81 – 82 – 83 – 84

82 – 83 – 84 – 85 – 86

86 – 87 – 88 – 89 – 90

Numbers up to 90 ⑦

♠ **Count and write the number of objects.**

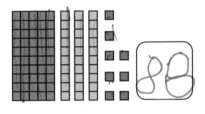 88

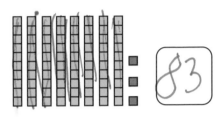 83

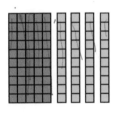 90

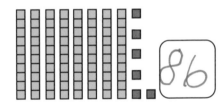 86

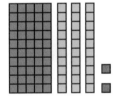 82

 84

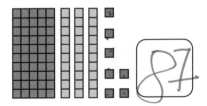 87

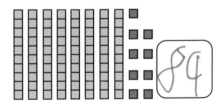 85

♠ Count and write the numbers of objects.

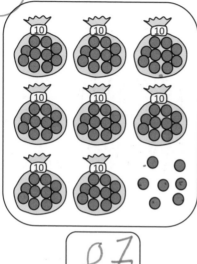

87

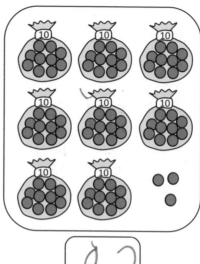

83

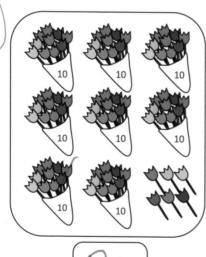

86

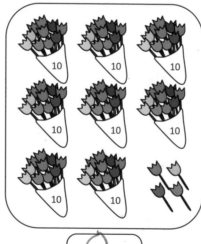

84

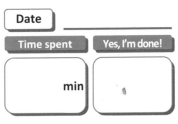

88 Numbers up to 90 ⑧

♠ **Write the missing numbers.**

81	82	83	84	85
86	87	88	89	90

81	82	83	84	85
86	87	88	89	90

81	82	83	84	85
86	87	88	89	90

♠ Write the missing numbers.

71	72	73	74	75
76	77	78	79	80
81	82	83	84	85
86	87	88	84	90
91	92	93	94	95
96	97	98	99	100

♠ Rewrite the given numbers from the smallest to the largest.

87   83   90   81

81 — 83 — 87 — 90

♠ **Count and write the number of objects.**

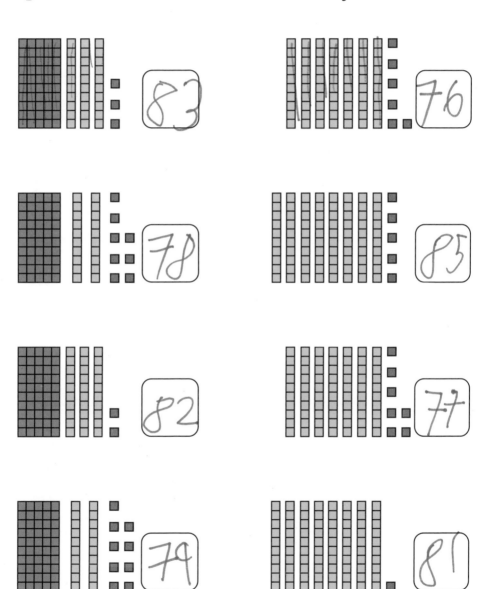

83

76

78

85

82

77

79

81

♠ **Write the missing numbers.**

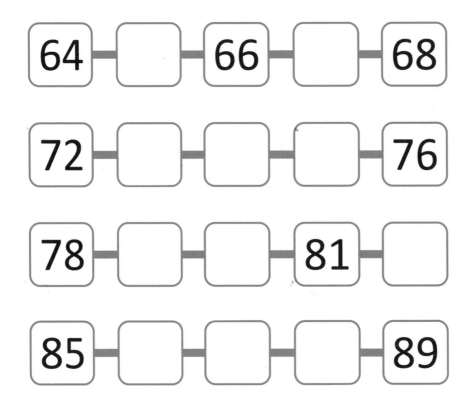

64 – ⬚ – 66 – ⬚ – 68

72 – ⬚ – ⬚ – ⬚ – 76

78 – ⬚ – ⬚ – 81 – ⬚

85 – ⬚ – ⬚ – ⬚ – 89

♠ **Rewrite the given numbers from the smallest to the largest.**

85   72   82   78

⬚ – ⬚ – ⬚ – ⬚

90 **Numbers up to 90 ⑩**

♠ **Write the missing numbers.**

61	62	63		65
66		68	69	

71		73	74	
76	77		79	80

	82	83	84	85
86		88		90

♠ Write the missing numbers.

61 — [ ] — 63 — 64 — [ ]

70 — 69 — [ ] — 67 — 66

[ ] — 72 — 73 — [ ] — 75

80 — 79 — 78 — 77 — [ ]

81 — [ ] — [ ] — 84 — 85

[ ] — 89 — 88 — 87 — 86

Week 2

This week's goal is to practice counting, writing, reading, and ordering numbers up to 110.

Tiger Session

Monday	91	92
Tuesday	93	94
Wednesday	95	96
Thursday	97	98
Friday	99	100

Date _____

Time spent | Yes, I'm done!

min

♠ Count and write the number of objects.

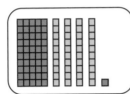

91

Ninety one

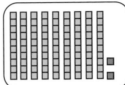

Ninety two

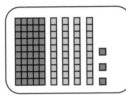

Ninety three

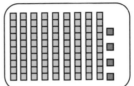

Ninety four

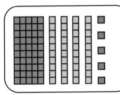

Ninety five

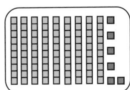

Ninety six

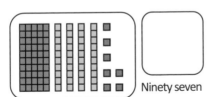

Ninety seven

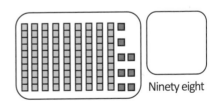

Ninety eight

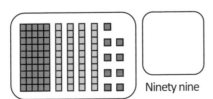

Ninety nine

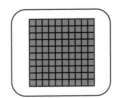

100

One hundred

♠ Count and write the number of objects.

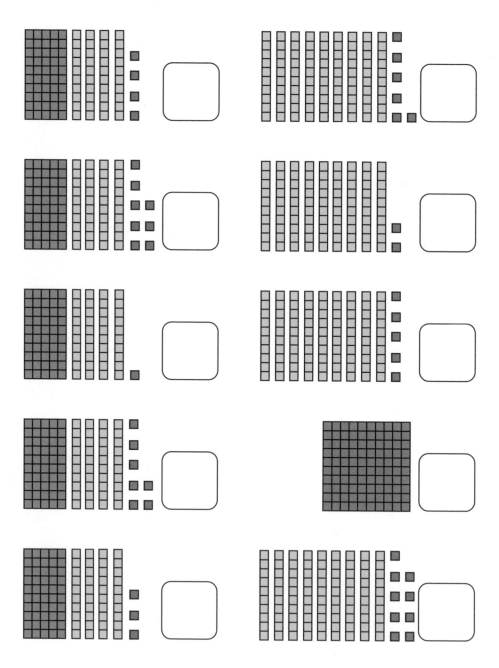

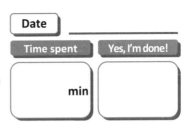

Date _____

Time spent | Yes, I'm done!
min

♠ Write the number which comes right <u>after</u> the given number.

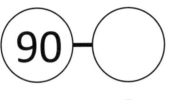

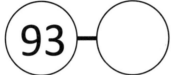

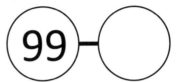

♠ Write the number which comes right <u>before</u> the given number.

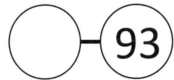

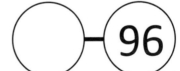

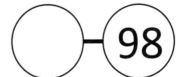

♠ Write the missing numbers.

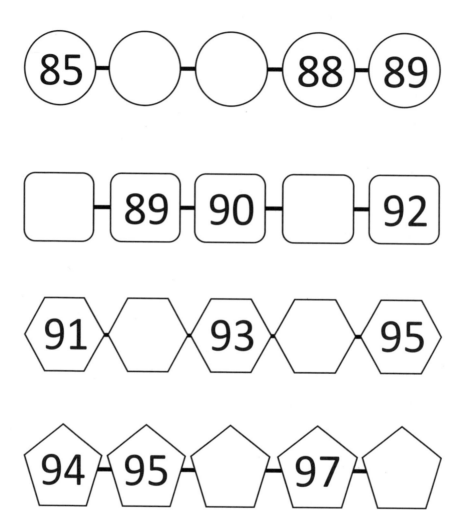

85 — ◯ — ◯ — 88 — 89

☐ — 89 — 90 — ☐ — 92

91 — ◇ — 93 — ◇ — 95

94 — 95 — ⬠ — 97 — ⬠

96 — ☐ — 98 — ☐ — 100

93 Numbers up to 110 ③

♠ Count and write the number of objects.

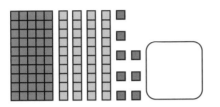

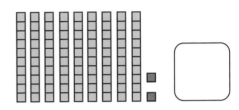

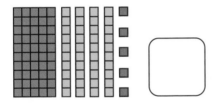

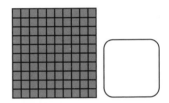

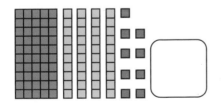

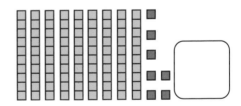

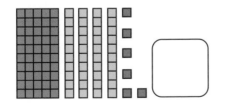

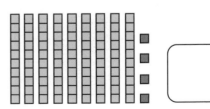

♠ **Count and write the numbers of objects.**

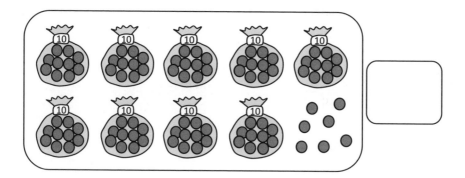

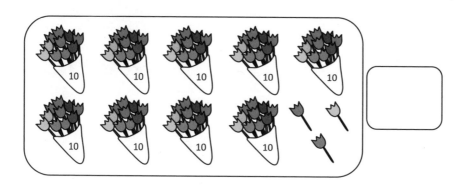

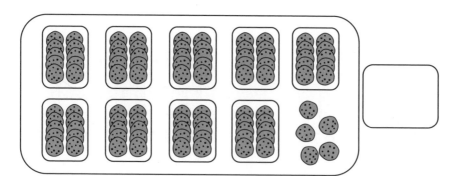

Date _____

Time spent | Yes, I'm done!

min

♠ **Write the missing numbers.**

91	92		94	95
	97		99	100

	92	93		95
96		98	99	100

91		93	94	
96	97	98		100

♠ Write the missing numbers.

81		83	84	85
86	87	88		90
	92	93	94	
96			99	100
101	102	103	104	105
106	107	108	109	110

♠ Rewrite the given numbers from the smallest to the largest.

94   93   95   92

95 Numbers up to 110 ⑤

♠ Count and write the number of objects.

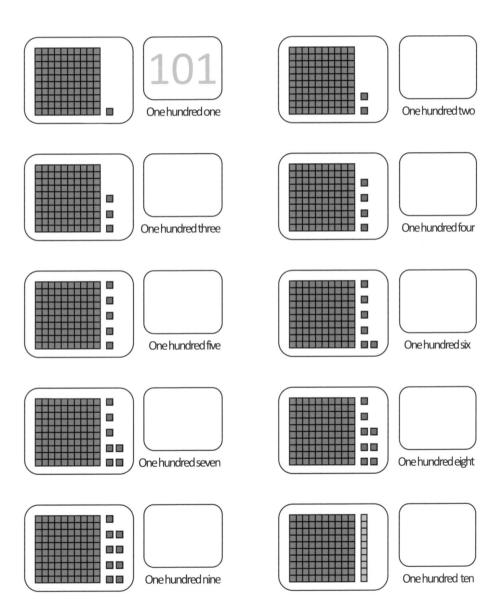

101
One hundred one

One hundred two

One hundred three

One hundred four

One hundred five

One hundred six

One hundred seven

One hundred eight

One hundred nine

One hundred ten

♠ **Count and write the number of objects.**

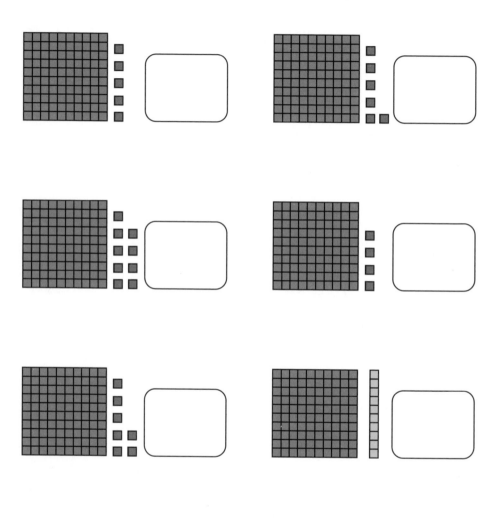

96 Numbers up to 110 ⑥

♠ Write the number which comes right <u>after</u> the given number.

♠ Write the number which comes right <u>before</u> the given number.

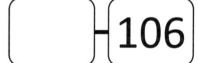

♠ **Write the missing numbers.**

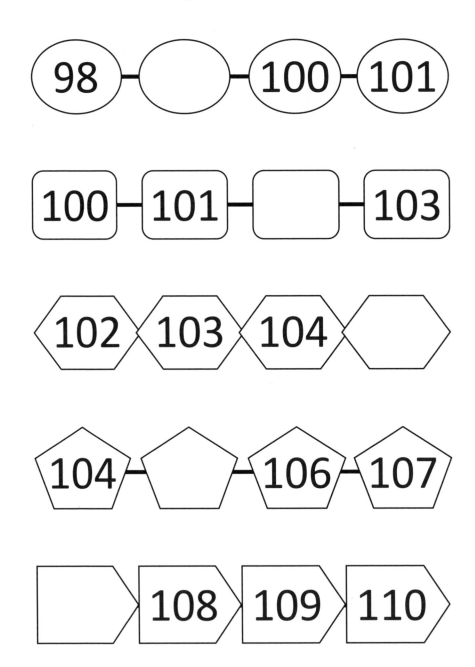

98 — ( ) — 100 — 101

100 — 101 — ( ) — 103

102 ⟩ 103 ⟩ 104 ⟩ ( )

104 — ( ) — 106 — 107

( ) ⟩ 108 ⟩ 109 ⟩ 110

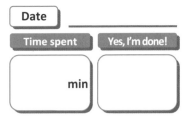

♠ **Count and write the number of objects.**

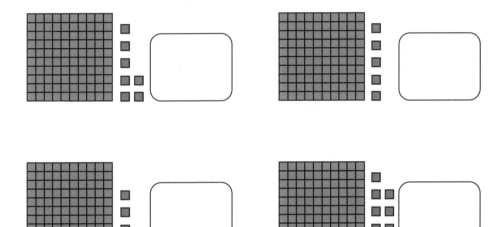

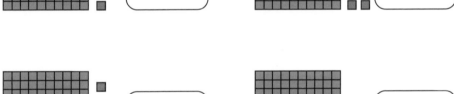

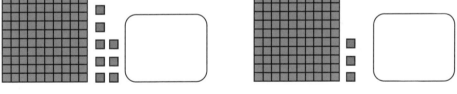

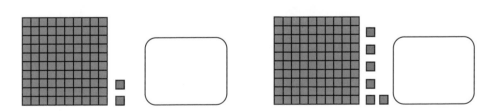

♠ **Count and write the numbers of objects.**

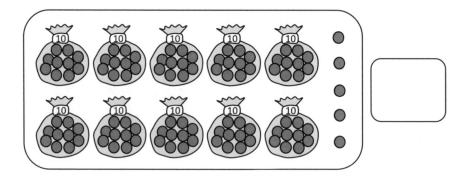

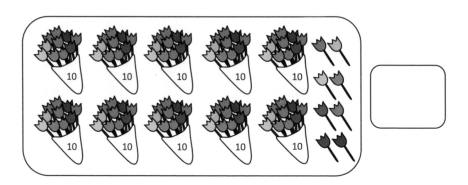

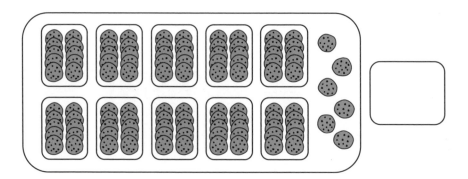

98 Numbers up to 110 ⑧

♠ Write the missing numbers.

81		83		85
86	87		89	90

91	92		94	95
96		98		100

101	102	103	104	
	107	108	109	

Write the missing numbers.

91	92	93		95
96	97		99	100
	102	103	104	
106	107	108		110
111	112	113	114	115
116	117	118	119	120

♠ Rewrite the given numbers from the smallest to the largest.

101   84   108   97

[ ]—[ ]—[ ]—[ ]

♠ **Count and write the number of objects.**

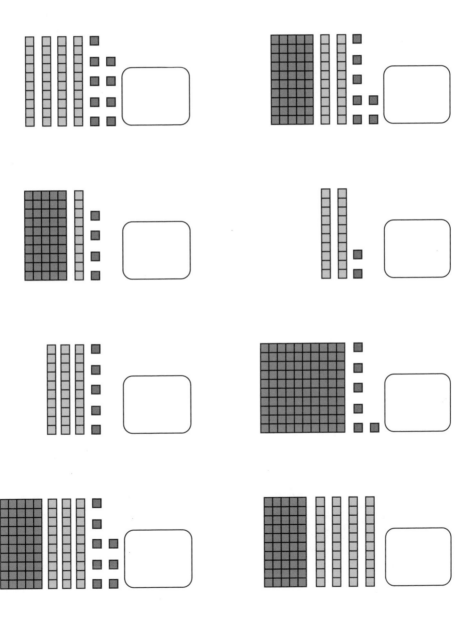

♠ Write the missing numbers.

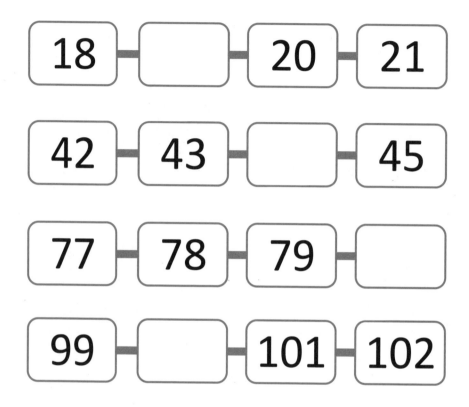

| 18 | | 20 | 21 |

| 42 | 43 | | 45 |

| 77 | 78 | 79 | |

| 99 | | 101 | 102 |

♠ Rewrite the given numbers from the smallest to the largest.

89   101   92   56

| | | | |

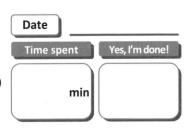

Date _____

Time spent | Yes, I'm done!

min

♠ **Write the missing numbers.**

31			34	35
36	37	38		40

	82	83		85
86	87		89	90

101	102	103	104	
106		108	109	

♠ **Write the missing numbers.**

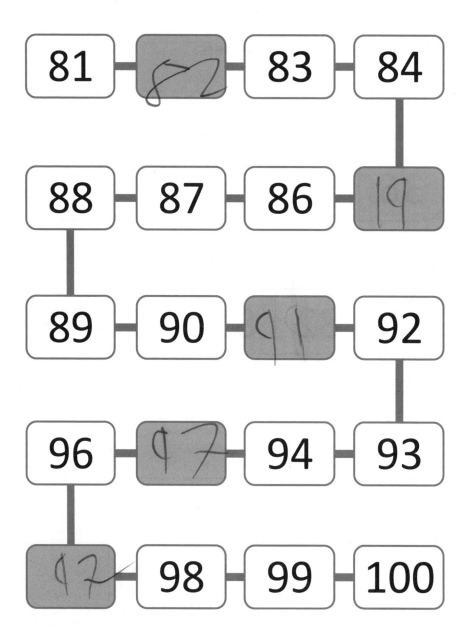

| 81 | 82 | 83 | 84 |

| 88 | 87 | 86 | 19 |

| 89 | 90 | 91 | 92 |

| 96 | 97 | 94 | 93 |

| 97 | 98 | 99 | 100 |

Week 3

This week's goals are
1) to understand the concept of addition, and
2) to practice adding 1 to the numbers in between 1 and 15.

Tiger Session

Monday	101	102
Tuesday	103	104
Wednesday	105	106
Thursday	107	108
Friday	109	110

Adding 1 ①

♠ **Read the numbers out lout and fill in the box with the missing number.**

(1) | 1 | 2 | 3 | 4 | 5 |

(2) | 6 | 7 | 8 | 9 | 10 |

(3) | 11 | 12 | 13 | 14 | 15 |

(4) | 16 | 17 | 18 | 19 | 20 |

(5) | 21 | 22 | 23 | 24 | 25 |

(6) | 26 | 27 | 28 | 29 | 30 |

(7) | 31 | 32 | 33 | 34 | 35 |

(8) | 36 | 37 | 38 | 39 | 40 |

(9) | 41 | 42 | 43 | 44 | 45 |

(10) | 46 | 47 | 48 | 49 | 50 |

(11) | 51 | 52 | 53 | 54 | 55 |

(12) | 56 | 57 | 58 | 59 | 60 |

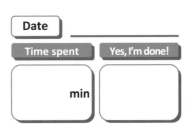

Date _____

Time spent | Yes, I'm done!

min

♠ **Read the numbers out lout and fill in the box with the missing number.**

(1) 61 — 62 — 63 — 64

(2) 65 — 66 — 67 — 68

(3) 69 — 70 — 71 — 72

(4) 73 — 74 — 75 — 76

(5) 77 — 78 — 79 — 80

(6) 81 — 82 — 83 — 84

(7) 85 — 86 — 87 — 88

(8) 89 — 90 — 91 — 92

(9) 93 — 94 — 95 — 96

(10) 97 — 98 — 99 — 100

(11) 101 — 102 — 103 — 104

(12) 105 — 106 — 107 — 108

(13) 109 — 110 — 111 — 112

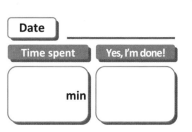

♠ **Fill in the box with the missing number.**

(1) 20 → 21 → 22 → 23

(2) 7 → 8 → 9 → 10

(3) 33 → 34 → 35 → 36

(4) 41 → 42 → 43 → 44

(5) 10 → 11 → 12 → 13

(6) 1 → 2 → 3 → 4

(7) 70 → 71 → 72 → 73

(8) 55 → 56 → 57 → 58

(9) 95 → 96 → 97 → 98

(10) 31 → 32 → 33 → 34

(11) 15 → 16 → 17 → 18

(12) 23 → 24 → 25 → 26

Adding 1 ④

♠ **Fill in the box with the missing number.**

(1) 20 → 21 → 22

(2) 33 → 34 → 35

(3) 15 → 16 → 17

(4) 28 → 29 → 30

(5) 10 → 11 → 12

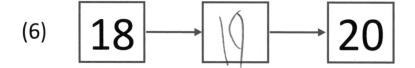

(6) | 18 | → | 19 | → | 20 |

(7) | 7 | → | 8 | → | 9 |

(8) | 45 | → | 46 | → | 47 |

(9) | 30 | → | 31 | → | 32 |

(10) | 12 | → | 13 | → | 14 |

(11) | 25 | → | 26 | → | 27 |

(12) | 17 | → | 18 | → | 19 |

Adding 1 ⑤

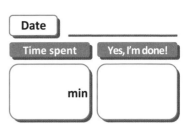

♠ **Fill in the box with the number which comes after the given number.**

(1) **9** ⟶ 10

(2) **3** ⟶ 4

(3) **18** ⟶ 19

(4) **27** ⟶ 28

(5) **37** ⟶ 38

(6)   25 ⟶ 26

(7)   56 ⟶ 57

(8)   22 ⟶ 23

(9)   14 ⟶ 15

(10) 32 ⟶ 34

(11) 4 ⟶ 5

(12) 50 ⟶ 51

Adding 1 ⑥

♠ **Fill in the box.**

(1) 1 ⟶ 2

   1 + 1 = 2

   one   plus   one   equals   two

(2) 2 ⟶ 3

   2 + 1 = 3

   two   plus   one   equals

(3) 3 ⟶ 4

   3 + 1 = 4

   three   plus   one   equals

(4)   4 ——————→   5

      4 + 1 =   5

      four plus one equals

(5)   5 ——————→   6

      5 + 1 =   6

      five plus one equals

(6)   6 ——————→   7

      6 + 1 =   7

      six plus one equals

(7)   7 ——————→   8

      7 + 1 =   8

      seven plus one equals

107 Adding 1 ⑦

♠ **Fill in the box.**

(1) 2 ⟶ $\boxed{3}$

2 + 1 = $\boxed{3}$

two plus one equals

(2) 4 ⟶ $\boxed{5}$

4 + 1 = $\boxed{5}$

four plus one equals

(3) 6 ⟶ $\boxed{7}$

6 + 1 = $\boxed{7}$

six plus one equals

(4) 3 ⟶ 4

3 + 1 = 4
three plus one equals

(5) 5 ⟶ 6

5 + 1 = 6
five plus one equals

(6) 7 ⟶ 8

7 + 1 = 8
seven plus one equals

(7) 9 ⟶ 10

9 + 1 = 10
nine plus one equals

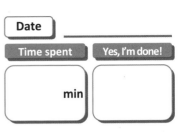

♠ **Fill in the box.**

(1) 6 ⟶ 7

 6 + 1 = 7

(2) 8 ⟶ 9

 8 + 1 = 9

(3) 10 ⟶ 11

 10 + 1 = 11

(4) 9 + 1 = 10

(5) 4 + 1 = 5

(6) 7 + 1 = 8

(7) 5 + 1 = 6

(8) 2 + 1 = 3

(9) 3 + 1 = 4

(10) 8 + 1 = 9

♠ **Add.**

(1) $2 + \bullet = 3$

(2) $4 + \bullet = 5$

(3) $6 + \bullet = 7$

(4) $8 + \bullet = 9$

(5) $10 + \bullet = 11$

(6) $3 + \bullet = 4$

(7)   5 + [•] = $\boxed{6}$

(8)   7 + [•] = $\boxed{8}$

(9)   9 + [•] = $\boxed{10}$

(10)   11 + [•] = $\boxed{12}$

(11)   13 + [•] = $\boxed{14}$

(12)   15 + [•] = $\boxed{16}$

Adding 1 ⑩

♠ **Add.**

(1) 5 + 1 = 6

(2) 8 + 1 = 9

(3) 6 + 1 = 7

(4) 3 + 1 = 4

(5) 7 + 1 = 8

(6) 4 + 1 = 5

♠ **Add.**

(7)

= | 11 | + | 1 | = | 12 |

(8)

= | 15 | + | 1 | = | 16 |

Week 4

This week's goals are
1) to understand the concept of addition, and
2) to practice adding 2 to the numbers in between 1 and 15.

Tiger Session

Monday	111	112
Tuesday	113	114
Wednesday	115	116
Thursday	117	118
Friday	119	120

Adding 2 ①

♠ **Fill in the box with the missing number.**

(1) | 2 | 3 | 4 |

(2) | 5 | 6 | 7 |

(3) | 8 | 9 | 10 |

(4) | 11 | 12 | 13 |

(5) | 14 | 15 | 16 |

(6) | 17 | 18 | 19 |

(7) 20 — 21 — 22

(8) 23 — 24 — 25

(9) 26 — 27 — 28

(10) 29 — 30 — 31

(11) 32 — 33 — 34

(12) 35 — 36 — 37

(13) 38 — 39 — 40

(14) 41 — 42 — 43

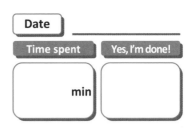

♠ **Fill in the box with the missing number.**

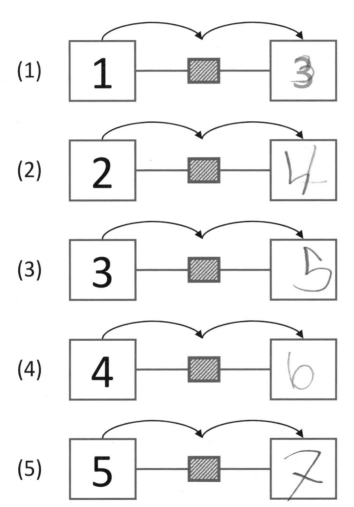

(1) 1 ▨ 3

(2) 2 ▨ 4

(3) 3 ▨ 5

(4) 4 ▨ 6

(5) 5 ▨ 7

 Tip: Think about what comes after adding 2.

(6) 6 —▨— 8

(7) 7 —▨— 9

(8) 8 —▨— 10

(9) 9 —▨— 11

(10) 10 —▨— 12

(11) 11 —▨— 13

(12) 12 —▨— 14

Date _____

Time spent | Yes, I'm done!

min

♠ **Fill in the box with the missing number.**

(1) 2 → ▨ → 4

(2) 4 → ▨ → 7

(3) 6 → ▨ → 8

(4) 8 → ▨ → 10

(5) 10 → ▨ → 12

(6) 12 → ▨ → 14

(7) 5 → [ ] → 7

(8) 7 → [ ] → 9

(9) 9 → [ ] → 11

(10) 11 → [ ] → 13

(11) 13 → [ ] → 15

(12) 15 → [ ] → 17

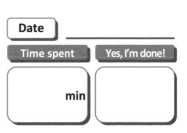

♠ **Fill in the box with the missing number.**

(1)

| 1 | → | ▨ | → | 3 |

1 + 2 = 3
one plus two equals

(2)

| 2 | → | ▨ | → | 4 |

2 + 2 = 4
two plus two equals

(3)

| 3 | → | ▨ | → | 5 |

3 + 2 = 5
three plus two equals

(4)

| 4 | → ▨ → | 6 |

4 + 2 = 6

(5)

| 5 | → ▨ → | 7 |

5 + 2 = 7

(6)

| 6 | → ▨ → | 8 |

6 + 2 = 8

(7)

| 7 | → ▨ → | 9 |

7 + 2 = 9

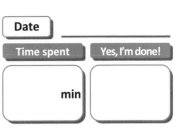

Date _____

Time spent | Yes, I'm done!

min

♠ **Add.**

(1) [7] → ▨ → ▨

$$7 + 2 = \boxed{9}$$

(2) [8] → ▨ → ▨

$$8 + 2 = \boxed{10}$$

(3) [9] → ▨ → ▨

$$9 + 2 = \boxed{11}$$

(4) [10] → ▨ → ▨

$$10 + 2 = \boxed{12}$$

(5)

11 → □ → □

11 + 2 = 13

(6)

12 → □ → □

12 + 2 = 14

(7)

13 → □ → □

13 + 2 = 15

(8)

14 → □ → □

14 + 2 = 16

(9)

15 → □ → □

15 + 2 = 17

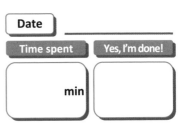

Date _____

Time spent   Yes, I'm done!

min

♠ **Add.**

(1) 8 → →

$$8 + 2 = \boxed{10}$$

(2) 10 → →

$$10 + 2 = \boxed{12}$$

(3) 12 → →

$$12 + 2 = \boxed{14}$$

(4) 14 → →

$$14 + 2 = \boxed{16}$$

(5)   [5] ⟶ ▨ ⟶ ▨

$$5 + 2 = \boxed{7}$$

(6)   [7] ⟶ ▨ ⟶ ▨

$$7 + 2 = \boxed{9}$$

(7)   [9] ⟶ ▨ ⟶ ▨

$$9 + 2 = \boxed{11}$$

(8)   [11] ⟶ ▨ ⟶ ▨

$$11 + 2 = \boxed{13}$$

(9)   [13] ⟶ ▨ ⟶ ▨

$$13 + 2 = \boxed{15}$$

Adding 2 ⑦

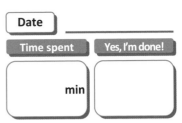

♠ **Add.**

(1) 5 ⟶ ⬛ ⟶ ⬛

$$5 + 2 = \boxed{7}$$

(2) 3 ⟶ ⬛ ⟶ ⬛

$$3 + 2 = \boxed{5}$$

(3) 10 ⟶ ⬛ ⟶ ⬛

$$10 + 2 = \boxed{12}$$

(4) 8 ⟶ ⬛ ⟶ ⬛

$$8 + 2 = \boxed{10}$$

(5) 6 + 2 = [8]

(6) 5 + 2 = [7]

(7) 9 + 2 = [11]

(8) 4 + 2 = [6]

(9) 2 + 2 = [4]

(10) 7 + 2 = [9]

Adding 2 ⑧

♠ **Add.**

(1) $4 +$ ⚁ $= \boxed{6}$

(2) $9 +$ ⚁ $= \boxed{11}$

(3) $10 +$ ⚁ $= \boxed{12}$

(4) $3 +$ ⚁ $= \boxed{5}$

(5) $12 +$ ⚁ $= \boxed{14}$

(6) $7 +$ ⚁ $= \boxed{19}$

(7) 6 + •• = 8

(8) 11 + •• = 13

(9) 8 + •• = 10

(10) 2 + •• = 4

(11) 13 + •• = 15

(12) 5 + •• = 7

Adding 2 ⑨

♠ **Add.**

(1) $3 + 2 =$ 5

(2) $9 + 2 =$ 11

(3) $11 + 2 =$ 13

(4) $2 + 2 =$ 4

(5) $7 + 2 =$ 9

 Tip: *Use two red dots below the number 2 for addition.*

(6)   5 + 2 = $\boxed{7}$

(7)   8 + 2 = $\boxed{10}$

(8)   4 + 2 = $\boxed{6}$

(9)   13 + 2 = $\boxed{15}$

(10) 10 + 2 = $\boxed{12}$

(11) 6 + 2 = $\boxed{8}$

(12) 12 + 2 = $\boxed{14}$

♠ **Add.**

(1) $5 + 2 = \boxed{7}$

(2) $10 + 2 = \boxed{12}$

(3) $3 + 2 = \boxed{5}$

(4) $14 + 2 = \boxed{16}$

(5) $2 + 2 = \boxed{4}$

(6) $8 + 2 = \boxed{10}$

♠ **Add.**

(7)

= P + 2 = 12

(8)

= 12 + 2 = 14

A – 3: Answers

Week 3

101 (p. 49 ~ 50)
① 3　② 7　③ 14　④ 20　⑤ 22
⑥ 26　⑦ 32　⑧ 40　⑨ 44　⑩ 47
⑪ 53　⑫ 59

102 (p. 51 ~ 52)
① 62　② 65　③ 70　④ 75　⑤ 80
⑥ 83　⑦ 86　⑧ 89　⑨ 94　⑩ 99
⑪ 104　⑫ 107　⑬ 110

103 (p. 53 ~ 54)
① 23　② 8　③ 33　④ 43　⑤ 11
⑥ 4　⑦ 72　⑧ 55　⑨ 96　⑩ 33
⑪ 18　⑫ 25

104 (p. 55 ~ 56)
① 21　② 34　③ 16　④ 29　⑤ 11
⑥ 19　⑦ 8　⑧ 46　⑨ 31　⑩ 13
⑪ 26　⑫ 18

105 (p. 57 ~ 58)
① 10　② 4　③ 19　④ 28　⑤ 38
⑥ 26　⑦ 57　⑧ 23　⑨ 15　⑩ 33
⑪ 5　⑫ 51

106 (p. 59 ~ 60)
① 2, 2　② 3, 3　③ 4, 4　④ 5, 5
⑤ 6, 6　⑥ 7, 7　⑦ 8, 8

107 (p. 61 ~ 62)
① 3, 3　② 5, 5　③ 7, 7　④ 4, 4
⑤ 6, 6　⑥ 8, 8　⑦ 10, 10

108 (p. 63 ~ 64)
① 7,7　② 9,9　③ 11,11　④ 10　⑤ 5
⑥ 8　⑦ 6　⑧ 3　⑨ 4　⑩ 9

109 (p. 65 ~ 66)
① 3　② 5　③ 7　④ 9　⑤ 11
⑥ 4　⑦ 6　⑧ 8　⑨ 10　⑩ 12
⑪ 14　⑫ 16

110 (p. 67 ~ 68)
① 6　② 9　③ 7　④ 4　⑤ 8
⑥ 5　⑦ 11 + 1 = 12　⑧ 15 + 1 = 16

Week 4

111 (p. 71 ~ 72)
① 4　② 7　③ 10　④ 13　⑤ 16
⑥ 19　⑦ 22　⑧ 25　⑨ 28　⑩ 31
⑪ 34　⑫ 37　⑬ 40　⑭ 43

112 (p. 73 ~ 74)
① 3　② 4　③ 5　④ 6　⑤ 7
⑥ 8　⑦ 9　⑧ 10　⑨ 11　⑩ 12
⑪ 13　⑫ 14

113 (p. 75 ~ 76)
① 4　② 6　③ 8　④ 10　⑤ 12
⑥ 14　⑦ 7　⑧ 9　⑨ 11　⑩ 13
⑪ 15　⑫ 17

114 (p. 77 ~ 78)
① 3, 3　② 4, 4　③ 5, 5　④ 6, 6
⑤ 7, 7　⑥ 8, 8　⑦ 9, 9

115 (p. 79 ~ 80)
① 9　② 10　③ 11　④ 12　⑤ 13
⑥ 14　⑦ 15　⑧ 16　⑨ 17

116 (p. 81 ~ 82)
① 10　② 12　③ 14　④ 16　⑤ 7
⑥ 9　⑦ 11　⑧ 13　⑨ 15

117 (p. 83 ~ 84)
① 7　② 5　③ 12　④ 10　⑤ 8
⑥ 7　⑦ 11　⑧ 6　⑨ 4　⑩ 9

118	(p. 85 ~ 86)			
① 6	② 11	③ 12	④ 5	⑤ 14
⑥ 9	⑦ 8	⑧ 13	⑨ 10	⑩ 4
⑪ 15	⑫ 7			

119	(p. 87 ~ 88)			
① 5	② 11	③ 13	④ 4	⑤ 9
⑥ 7	⑦ 10	⑧ 6	⑨ 15	⑩ 12
⑪ 8	⑫ 14			

120	(p. 89 ~ 90)			
① 7	② 12	③ 5	④ 16	⑤ 4
⑥ 10	⑦ 9 + 2 = 11	⑧ 12 + 2 = 14		

Tiger Math

ACHIEVEMENT AWARD

THIS AWARD IS PRESENTED TO

_____

(student name)

FOR SUCESSFULLY COMPLETING

TIGER MATH LEVEL A – 3.

Dr. Tiger

_____

Dr.Tiger